March
with Me

Jump along, jump along,
jump along with me.

Stalk along, stalk along,
stalk along with me.

Crawl along, crawl along, crawl along with me.

4

Slide along, slide along,
slide along with me.

Stomp along, stomp along, stomp along with me.

Strut along, strut along,
strut along with me.

March along, march along,
march along with me.

8